HUNT FOR HECTOR

Anthony Tallarico

HUNT FOR HECTOR AT THE DOG HALL OF FAME AND....

- ☐ Alien
- ☐ Astronaut
- ☐ Babe Ruff
- ☐ 2 Birds
- ☐ Boot
- ☐ "Buffalo Bull"
- ☐ Cannon
- ☐ Car
- ☐ Cat
- ☐ "Cave Dog"
- ☐ Clown
- ☐ Cook
- ☐ "Down Boy"
- ☐ Elephant
- ☐ Fallen star
- ☐ Flying dog
- ☐ Ghost dog
- ☐ 2 Giant bones
- ☐ Guard dog
- ☐ Hot dog
- ☐ Husky
- ☐ Indian
- ☐ Juggler
- ☐ Kangaroo
- ☐ Man on leash
- ☐ Mirror
- ☐ Moon
- ☐ Mouse
- ☐ Napoleon
- ☐ Photographer
- ☐ Pilgrim
- ☐ Pirate flag
- ☐ Record player
- ☐ Rugby ball
- ☐ Santa hound
- ☐ Sheep
- ☐ Sherlock Bones
- ☐ Stamp
- ☐ Super hero
- ☐ Super poodle
- ☐ Target
- ☐ Tin can

HUNT FOR HECTOR AT DOG SCHOOL AND....

- ☐ A-ARF
- ☐ Artist's model
- ☐ Banana skin
- ☐ Blackboard cleaner
- ☐ Building plans
- ☐ Cat
- ☐ Chalk
- ☐ Clipboard
- ☐ Cloud
- ☐ Comic book
- ☐ Cook
- ☐ Cork
- ☐ Crown
- ☐ 2 Dancing dogs
- ☐ Doggy bag
- ☐ Doggy bank
- ☐ Dogwood
- ☐ Dunce's cap
- ☐ Fire hydrant
- ☐ Flying bone
- ☐ 2 Forks
- ☐ Frankendog
- ☐ Genie
- ☐ Graduate
- ☐ Hammer
- ☐ Handkerchief
- ☐ "Hi, Mum!"
- ☐ "History Of Bones"
- ☐ Hockey stick
- ☐ "How To Bark"
- ☐ Leash
- ☐ Mush
- ☐ 2 Pencils
- ☐ Postman
- ☐ P.T.A.
- ☐ Roller skates
- ☐ Saw
- ☐ 2 School bags
- ☐ Scooter
- ☐ Set-square
- ☐ Sun
- ☐ Sunglasses
- ☐ Triangle

HUNT FOR HECTOR
WHERE THE RICH
AND FAMOUS DOGS
LIVE AND....

- ☐ Admiral
- ☐ Airship
- ☐ Alligator
- ☐ Artist
- ☐ Bank
- ☐ "Big Wheel"
- ☐ Bird bath
- ☐ Bone chimney
- ☐ Candle
- ☐ Castle
- ☐ Cat
- ☐ 2 Cooks
- ☐ Crown
- ☐ Cushion
- ☐ Dog fish
- ☐ Dog flag
- ☐ Dog prince statue
- ☐ 2 Dog-shaped bushes
- ☐ Door dog
- ☐ Fat dog
- ☐ Fire hydrant
- ☐ Fisherdog's catch
- ☐ Fizzy drink
- ☐ 2 Golfers
- ☐ Guard
- ☐ Heart
- ☐ Heron
- ☐ Human
- ☐ 3 Joggers
- ☐ 6 Limousines
- ☐ Periscope
- ☐ Pool
- ☐ Star
- ☐ "Superior Flats"
- ☐ Tennis player
- ☐ TV aerial
- ☐ Umbrella
- ☐ Violinist
- ☐ Water-skier
- ☐ Whale

HUNT FOR HECTOR AT THE K-9 CLEANUP AND....

HUNT FOR HECTOR AT THE SUPER DOG BOWL AND....

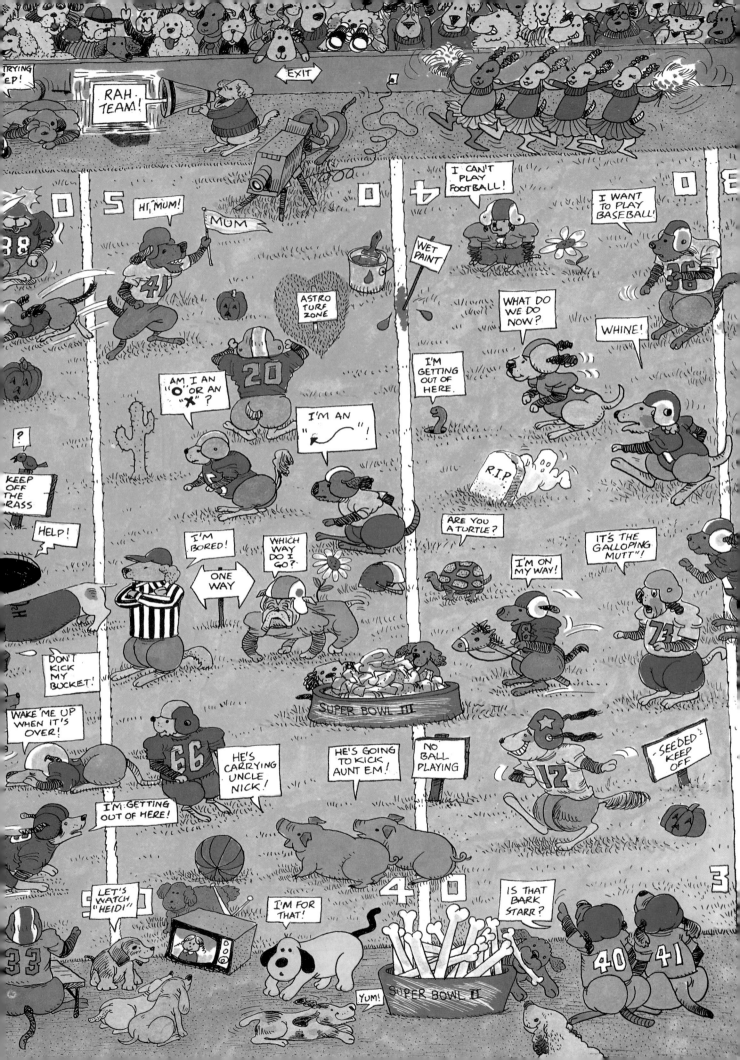

HUNT FOR HECTOR
AT THE DOG
SHOPPING MALL
AND....

- ☐ Ball
- ☐ Balloon
- ☐ Barber's shop
- ☐ Bat
- ☐ Bird's house
- ☐ 2 Biscuits
- ☐ Candle
- ☐ 2 Cats
- ☐ Cheerleader
- ☐ Clown
- ☐ Cup
- ☐ Dog bowls "Sale"
- ☐ Dog cake
- ☐ Fish
- ☐ Flamingo
- ☐ Ghost
- ☐ Headphones
- ☐ Heart
- ☐ Helmet
- ☐ Howling dog
- ☐ Human
- ☐ Ice cream cone
- ☐ Kennel
- ☐ Knight in armour
- ☐ 2 Litter bins
- ☐ Lollipop
- ☐ Mask
- ☐ Mouse
- ☐ Newsdog
- ☐ Newspaper reader
- ☐ Nut
- ☐ Paper aeroplane
- ☐ Pelican
- ☐ Pizza slice
- ☐ Police dog
- ☐ Pumpkin
- ☐ Scarf
- ☐ Stool
- ☐ Sugar stick
- ☐ Sunglasses
- ☐ Tennis racquet
- ☐ Tyre
- ☐ Trophy
- ☐ Waiter

HUNT FOR HECTOR AT THE DOG OLYMPICS AND....

- ☐ Archer
- ☐ 7 Arrows
- ☐ Basketball
- ☐ Batter
- ☐ Bomb
- ☐ Bone balloon
- ☐ Boomerang
- ☐ Broom
- ☐ Caddy
- ☐ Car chase
- ☐ Cyclists
- ☐ Dunce's cap
- ☐ Fencers
- ☐ "Fetch"
- ☐ Fish
- ☐ Football
- ☐ "Go Dogs"
- ☐ Golf ball
- ☐ Gymnasts
- ☐ "Hi, Mum"
- ☐ Hockey game
- ☐ Horse
- ☐ Horseshoe
- ☐ Ice cream cone
- ☐ Karate chop
- ☐ Lacrosse stick
- ☐ Paper aeroplane
- ☐ Pole vaulter
- ☐ Rower
- ☐ Skateboard
- ☐ Skier
- ☐ 2 Sleeping dogs
- ☐ Snow dog
- ☐ Soccer ball
- ☐ Starter's gun
- ☐ "Stop"
- ☐ Target
- ☐ Trainer
- ☐ TV camera
- ☐ "Very Thin Ice"
- ☐ Weight lifter
- ☐ Yo-yo

HUNT FOR HECTOR IN SPACE AND....

- ☐ Bark Vader
- ☐ Bed
- ☐ Boat
- ☐ "Boney Way"
- ☐ Book
- ☐ "Bow-Wow Land"
- ☐ Boxing glove
- ☐ Cat
- ☐ "Dog catcher"
- ☐ Dog fish
- ☐ Dog graduate
- ☐ "Dog trek"
- ☐ "Doggy bag"
- ☐ "Duck Rogers"
- ☐ "Emergency stop"
- ☐ Fire hydrant
- ☐ Flying food dish
- ☐ Flying kennel
- ☐ Hot dog
- ☐ Jail
- ☐ Kite
- ☐ Launch site
- ☐ "Lost and Found"
- ☐ Map
- ☐ Moon dog
- ☐ "No Barking"
- ☐ Parachute
- ☐ Pirate
- ☐ Pizza
- ☐ Planet of the bones
- ☐ Planet of the dogs
- ☐ Police dog
- ☐ Postman
- ☐ "Pup tent"
- ☐ "Puppy trainer"
- ☐ Robot dog
- ☐ Saint Bernard
- ☐ Sleeping dog
- ☐ Space circus
- ☐ Surfboard
- ☐ Swimming pool
- ☐ Tyre
- ☐ Unicycle
- ☐ Vampire dog
- ☐ Vanishing dog

HUNT FOR HECTOR IN DOGTOWN AND....

- [ ] "The Arf Building"
- [ ] Barbecue
- [ ] Bird bath
- [ ] Boat
- [ ] Bone crop
- [ ] Bookstore
- [ ] 2 Broken clocks
- [ ] 8 Broken windows
- [ ] 2 Cats
- [ ] "Curb Your Human"
- [ ] Dance studio
- [ ] Dog bone letterbox
- [ ] 5 Fire hydrants
- [ ] Flag
- [ ] "For Rent"
- [ ] Fountain
- [ ] "Frozen Dog Food"
- [ ] "Happy Dog Mush"
- [ ] 3 Hard hats
- [ ] Ice cream lorry
- [ ] Illegally parked car
- [ ] Jogger
- [ ] Lawn mower
- [ ] Mechanic
- [ ] Motorcycle
- [ ] Newsdog
- [ ] "People Catcher"
- [ ] Petrol station
- [ ] Piano
- [ ] Pool
- [ ] Post-dog
- [ ] "Preschool"
- [ ] Red trolley
- [ ] Santa Claus
- [ ] Sledge
- [ ] Sock
- [ ] Video shop
- [ ] Water tower
- [ ] Weather vane
- [ ] Window cleaner
- [ ] Witch
- [ ]

HUNT FOR HECTOR

SEARCH FOR SAM

FIND FREDDIE

LOOK FOR LIS